a Book of Numbers

by

Freddie McKeown

 Printed in England. ISBN 0 85503 149 2

1
one

one blue boat bobbing on the sea,
sailing solo in the sun ....
happy to be free !

2
two

a pair of pears, one and two,
one for me, and one for you!

3
three
three lazy bears,
all their work is done ,
spending the day lying in the sun!

4
four

four fine feathers all in a row,
when there's a puff of wind....
off they go!

5
five

five loaves of fresh bread
baked for a feast — to flour, salt
and water... add a pinch of yeast!

6
six

six speckled eggs
from a big brown hen ~ look again
tomorrow ... and there might be ten!

7
seven
seven sea shells
sifted from a sandy shore, listen....
can you hear the seven seas
once more.

8
eight
tinker
tailor
soldier
sailor
rich-man
thief
poor-man
beggar-man
eight tiny cherry stones
lined up round a plate,
tinker, tailor, soldier, sailor.....
... what will be my fate ?

9
nine

nine golden leaves lying on the ground,
a sign that autumn's coming ....
the year goes round and round.

ten green bottles not standing on a wall ~ that would be too silly, for one would surely fall !

15
fifteen

fifteen flying kites blown high
or low ~ they dive and soar
through the sky swooping
to and fro !

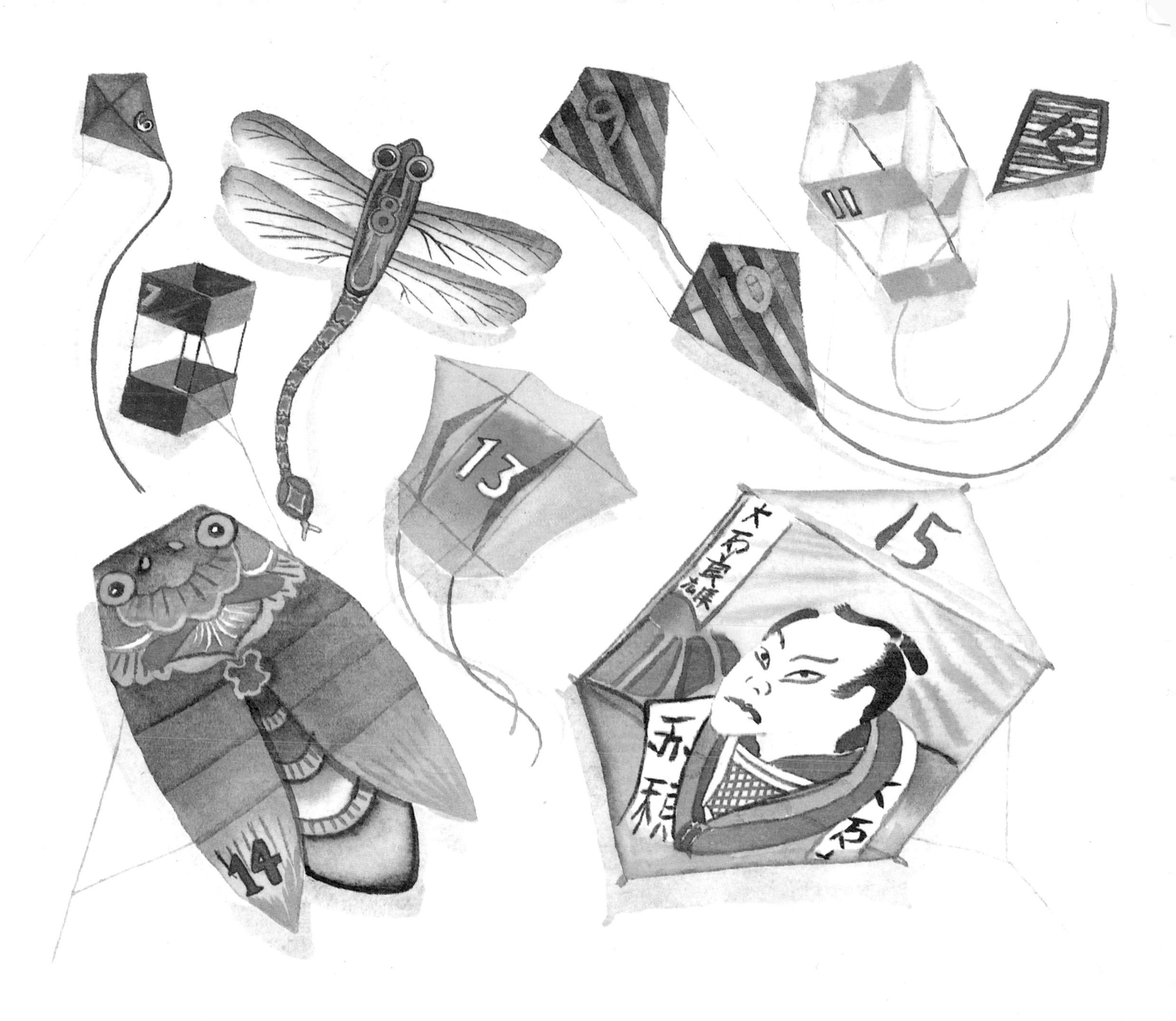
6
7
8
9
10
11
12
13
14
15

20
twenty

twenty tough toy soldiers lined
up on parade — dressed in
finest red coats ....
with medals all displayed !

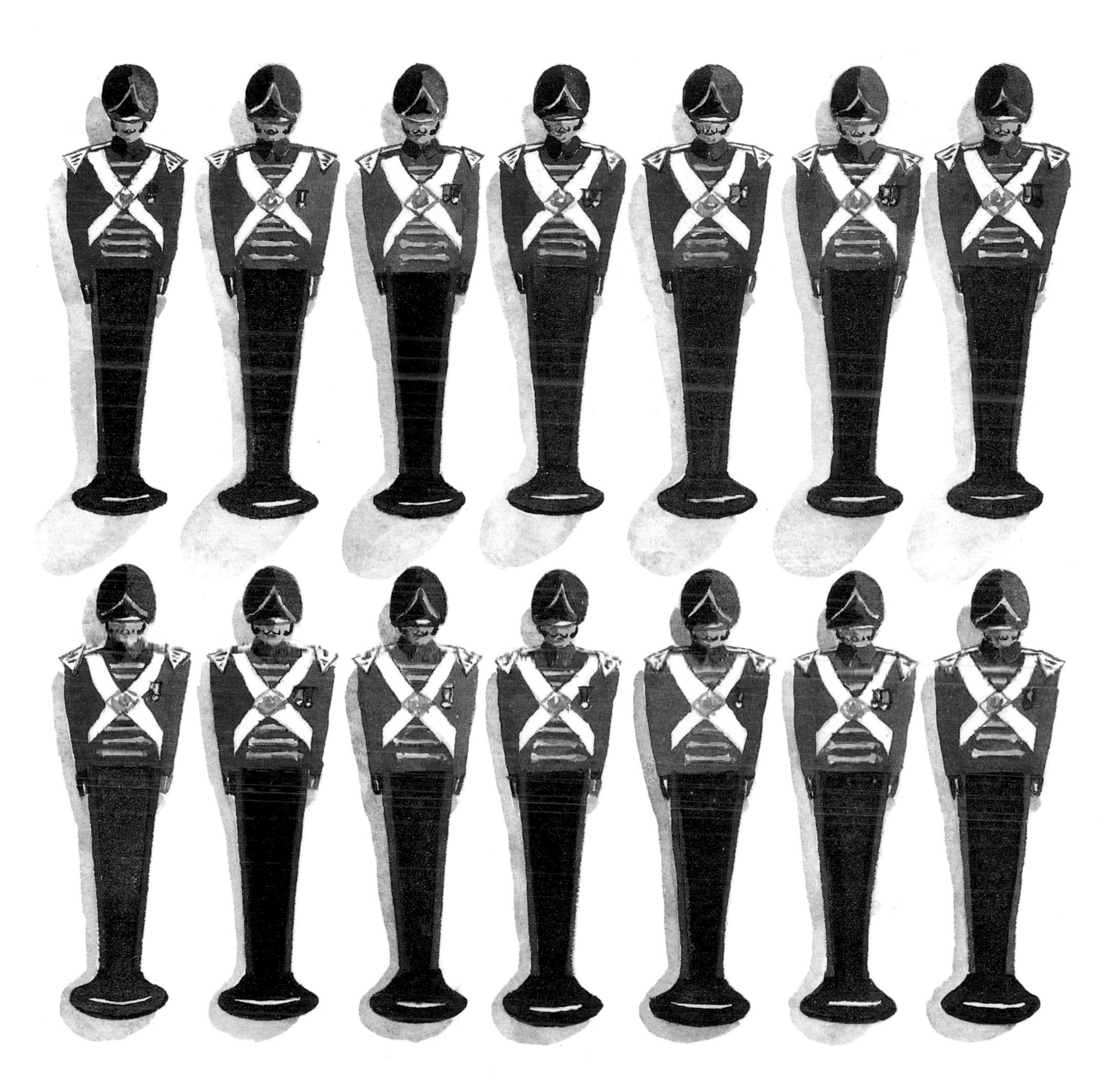

30
thirty

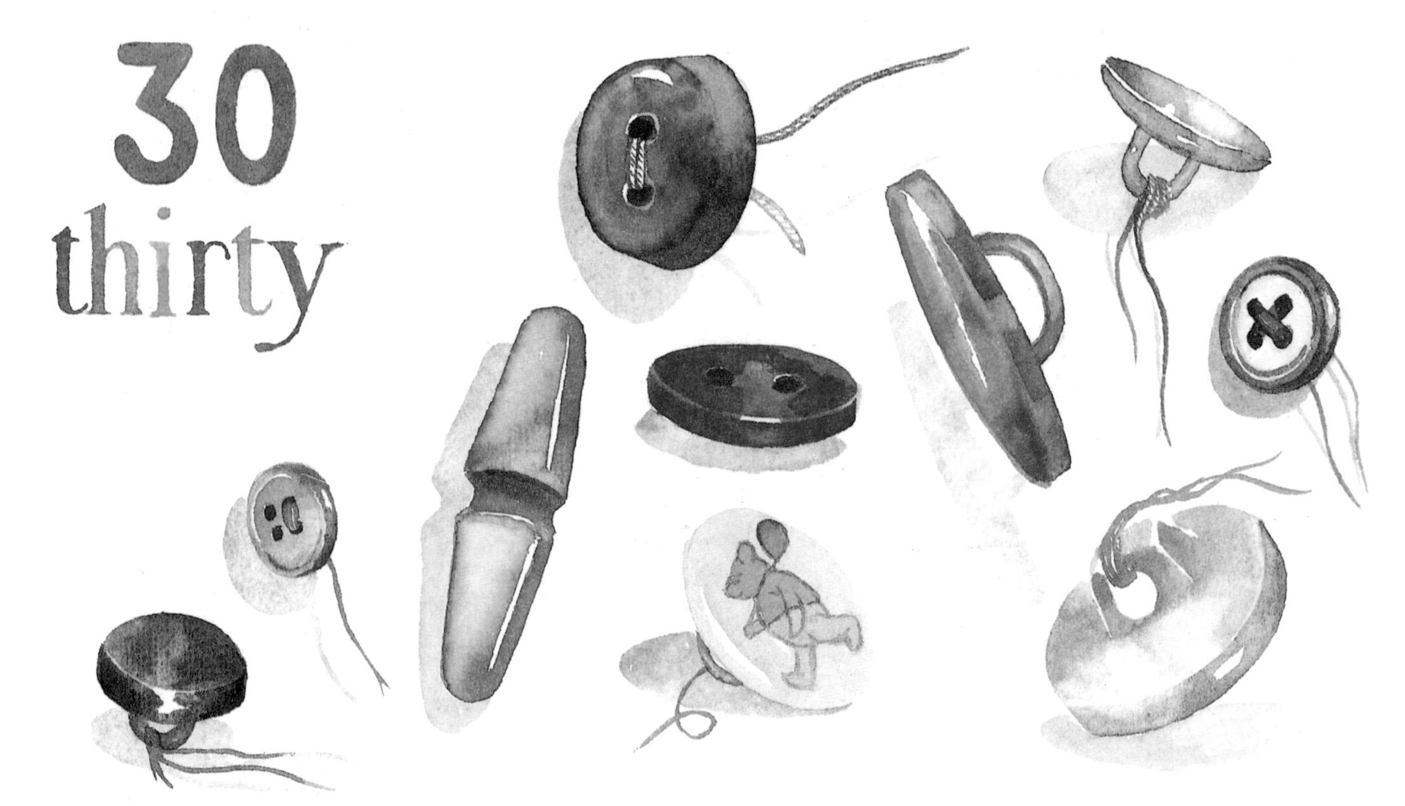

thirty threaded buttons for you
and me to sew — but which
clothes they all came off ....
we will never know !

40
forty

forty varied flower pots all
made out of clay.
waiting in the garden shed....
for a potting day !

50
fifty

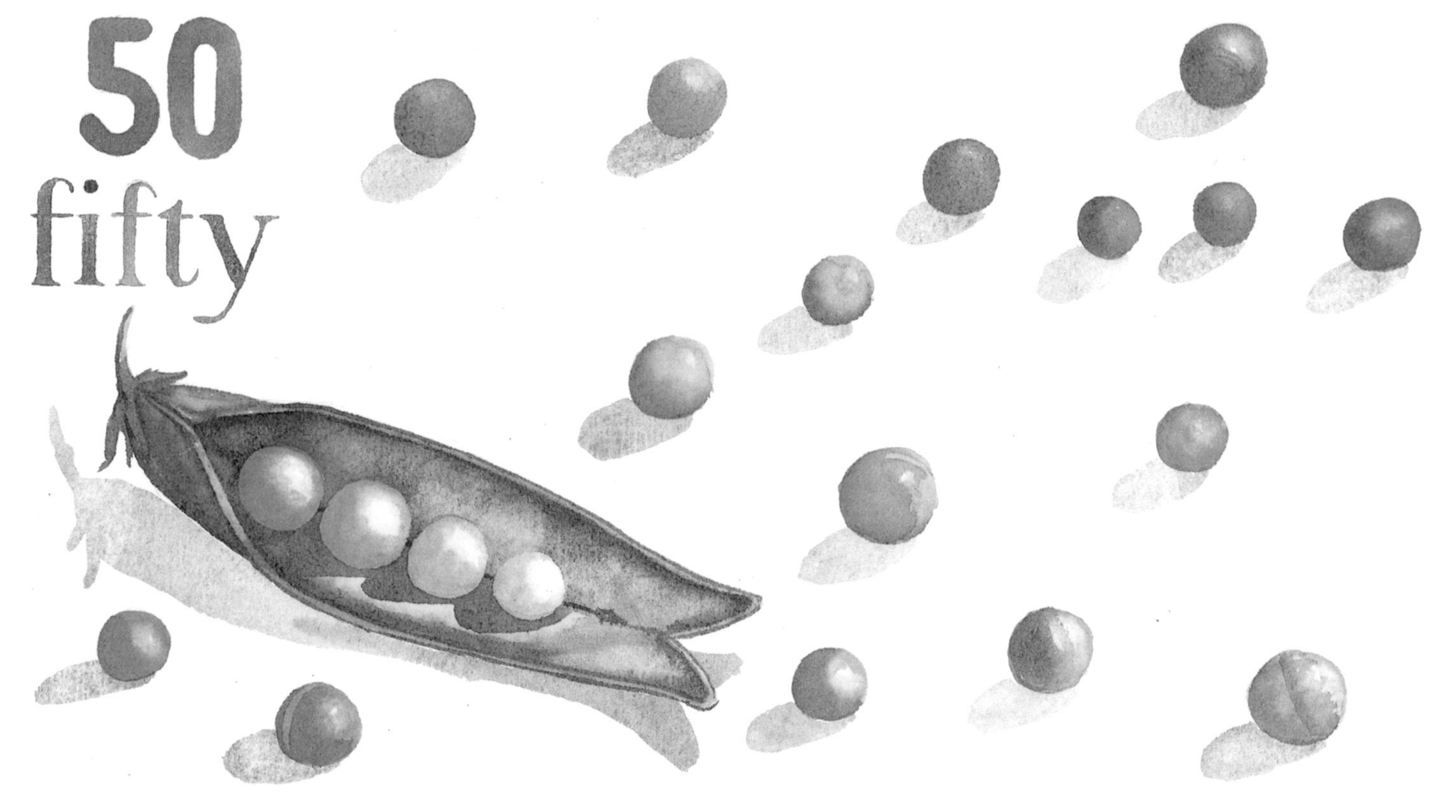

fifty firm green peas bursting
full of flavour — from the pod
or from the pan .... they are
always good to savour !

100
one hundred

one hundred bees are working
that's plain enough to see ....
flying here , buzzing there —
— as busy as can be !

too many to count . . .

I lost count at a thousand, or
maybe 'twas a million . . . .
the pebbles on the beach could
add up to a billion !